KaMille Stewart

TATE PUBLISHING
AND ENTERPRISES, LLC

Published by Tate Publishing & Enterprises, LLC
127 E. Trade Center Terrace | Mustang, Oklahoma 73064 USA
1.888.361.9473 | www.tatepublishing.com

Tate Publishing is committed to excellence in the publishing industry. The company reflects the philosophy established by the founders, based on Psalm 68:11,
"The Lord gave the word and great was the company of those who published it."

Book design copyright © 2013 by Tate Publishing, LLC. All rights reserved.
Cover design by Lauro Talibong
Interior design by Ronnel Luspoc

Published in the United States of America

ISBN: 978-1-62510-485-4
1. Religion / Christian Life
13.03.19

Acknowledgments

I would like to thank God for the vision and guidance to create this book. I would also like to thank my family, friends, and spiritual mentors for their encouragement and support throughout this process.

Contents

Introduction

In an effort to encourage and inspire Christians to become more resilient and mature in their Christian faith, this book was created to help Christians in their daily walk. It serves as an insight into our lives as we strive to become better people and better Christians.

Seven-Day Meditation and Reflection

Morning Meditation

Date: _____

What will be your prayer target today?

- Church

- Spiritual Leaders

- Family

- Government (country, state, or city)

- Marketplace

- The Unreached

- Destruction of Strongholds

- Other: _____

_____

_____

_____

_____

Inspirational Scriptures

Isaiah 40:31, Matthew 19:26, Philippians 4:19, Romans 8:28, John 14:27, Psalms 27:14, Matthew 6:33, Joshua 1:9, Matthew 6:25–27, Psalm 118:24, Proverbs 3:5–6, James 1:19–20, Isaiah 54:17, Psalm 51:10

Evening Reflection

Date: _____

What did you experience today?

_____

_____

_____

_____

If it was a good or bad experience, what was your reaction?

_____

_____

_____

Is this reaction in accordance with a Christian example?

_____

If yes, give scripture(s) that have guided you to your reaction?

_____

_____

If no, how could you have reacted differently, and what scripture(s) have you turned to for guidance?

_____

_____

_____

My Faith, My Walk

Supporting scripture(s):

_____

_____

_____

Inspirational Scriptures

1 Thessalonians 5:16–18, Philippians 4:6–7, Psalm 46:1, Galatians 6:9, James 1:2–3, Psalm 4:8, 2 Timothy 1:7, Jeremiah 29:11, Matthew 11:28, Psalm 121, Proverbs 16:3, Psalms 1:1–3 , Philippians 4:19, Psalm 51:12

Morning Meditation

Date: _____

What will be your prayer target today?

- Church

- Spiritual Leaders

- Family

- Government (country, state, or city)

- Marketplace

- The Unreached

- Destruction of Strongholds

- Other: _____

_____

_____

_____

_____

Inspirational Scriptures

Isaiah 40:31, Matthew 19:26, Philippians 4:19, Romans 8:28, John 14:27, Psalms 27:14, Matthew 6:33, Joshua 1:9, Matthew 6:25–27, Psalm 118:24, Proverbs 3:5–6, James 1:19–20, Isaiah 54:17, Psalm 51:10

Evening Reflection

Date: _____

What did you experience today?

_____

_____

_____

_____

If it was a good or bad experience, what was your reaction?

_____

_____

_____

Is this reaction in accordance with a Christian example?

_____

If yes, give scripture(s) that have guided you to your reaction?

_____

_____

If no, how could you have reacted differently, and what scripture(s) have you turned to for guidance?

_____

_____

_____

MY FAITH, MY WALK

Supporting scripture(s):

_____

_____

_____

Inspirational Scriptures

1 Thessalonians 5:16–18, Philippians 4:6–7, Psalm 46:1, Galatians 6:9, James 1:2–3, Psalm 4:8, 2 Timothy 1:7, Jeremiah 29:11, Matthew 11:28, Psalm 121, Proverbs 16:3, Psalms 1:1–3 , Philippians 4:19, Psalm 51:12

Morning Meditation

Date: _____

What will be your prayer target today?

- Church

- Spiritual Leaders

- Family

- Government (country, state, or city)

- Marketplace

- The Unreached

- Destruction of Strongholds

- Other: _____

_____

_____

_____

_____

Inspirational Scriptures
Isaiah 40:31, Matthew 19:26, Philippians 4:19, Romans 8:28, John 14:27, Psalms 27:14, Matthew 6:33, Joshua 1:9, Matthew 6:25–27, Psalm 118:24, Proverbs 3:5–6, James 1:19–20, Isaiah 54:17, Psalm 51:10

Evening Reflection

Date: _____

What did you experience today?

_____

_____

_____

_____

If it was a good or bad experience, what was your reaction?

_____

_____

_____

Is this reaction in accordance with a Christian example?

_____

If yes, give scripture(s) that have guided you to your reaction?

_____

_____

If no, how could you have reacted differently, and what scripture(s) have you turned to for guidance?

_____

_____

_____

Supporting scripture(s):

_____

_____

_____

Inspirational Scriptures

1 Thessalonians 5:16–18, Philippians 4:6–7, Psalm 46:1, Galatians 6:9, James 1:2–3, Psalm 4:8, 2 Timothy 1:7, Jeremiah 29:11, Matthew 11:28, Psalm 121, Proverbs 16:3, Psalms 1:1–3 , Philippians 4:19, Psalm 51:12

Morning Meditation

Date: _____

What will be your prayer target today?

- Church

- Spiritual Leaders

- Family

- Government (country, state, or city)

- Marketplace

- The Unreached

- Destruction of Strongholds

- Other: _____

_____

_____

_____

_____

Inspirational Scriptures

Isaiah 40:31, Matthew 19:26, Philippians 4:19, Romans 8:28, John 14:27, Psalms 27:14, Matthew 6:33, Joshua 1:9, Matthew 6:25–27, Psalm 118:24, Proverbs 3:5–6, James 1:19–20, Isaiah 54:17, Psalm 51:10

Evening Reflection

Date: _____

What did you experience today?

_____

_____

_____

_____

If it was a good or bad experience, what was your reaction?

_____

_____

_____

Is this reaction in accordance with a Christian example?

_____

If yes, give scripture(s) that have guided you to your reaction?

_____

_____

If no, how could you have reacted differently, and what scripture(s) have you turned to for guidance?

_____

_____

_____

Supporting scripture(s):

_____

_____

_____

Inspirational Scriptures

1 Thessalonians 5:16–18, Philippians 4:6–7, Psalm 46:1, Galatians 6:9, James 1:2–3, Psalm 4:8, 2 Timothy 1:7, Jeremiah 29:11, Matthew 11:28, Psalm 121, Proverbs 16:3, Psalms 1:1–3 , Philippians 4:19, Psalm 51:12

Morning Meditation

Date: _____

What will be your prayer target today?

- Church

- Spiritual Leaders

- Family

- Government (country, state, or city)

- Marketplace

- The Unreached

- Destruction of Strongholds

- Other: _____

_____

_____

_____

_____

Inspirational Scriptures

Isaiah 40:31, Matthew 19:26, Philippians 4:19, Romans 8:28, John 14:27, Psalms 27:14, Matthew 6:33, Joshua 1:9, Matthew 6:25–27, Psalm 118:24, Proverbs 3:5–6, James 1:19–20, Isaiah 54:17, Psalm 51:10

Evening Reflection

Date: _____

What did you experience today?

_____

_____

_____

_____

If it was a good or bad experience, what was your reaction?

_____

_____

_____

Is this reaction in accordance with a Christian example?

_____

If yes, give scripture(s) that have guided you to your reaction?

_____

_____

If no, how could you have reacted differently, and what scripture(s) have you turned to for guidance?

_____

_____

_____

Supporting scripture(s):

_____

_____

_____

Inspirational Scriptures

1 Thessalonians 5:16–18, Philippians 4:6–7, Psalm 46:1, Galatians 6:9, James 1:2–3, Psalm 4:8, 2 Timothy 1:7, Jeremiah 29:11, Matthew 11:28, Psalm 121, Proverbs 16:3, Psalms 1:1–3 , Philippians 4:19, Psalm 51:12

Morning Meditation

Date: _____

What will be your prayer target today?

- Church

- Spiritual Leaders

- Family

- Government (country, state, or city)

- Marketplace

- The Unreached

- Destruction of Strongholds

- Other: _____

_____

_____

_____

_____

Inspirational Scriptures

Isaiah 40:31, Matthew 19:26, Philippians 4:19, Romans 8:28, John 14:27, Psalms 27:14, Matthew 6:33, Joshua 1:9, Matthew 6:25–27, Psalm 118:24, Proverbs 3:5–6, James 1:19–20, Isaiah 54:17, Psalm 51:10

Evening Reflection

Date: _____

What did you experience today?

_____

_____

_____

_____

If it was a good or bad experience, what was your reaction?

_____

_____

_____

Is this reaction in accordance with a Christian example?

_____

If yes, give scripture(s) that have guided you to your reaction?

_____

_____

If no, how could you have reacted differently, and what scripture(s) have you turned to for guidance?

_____

_____

_____

MY FAITH, MY WALK

Supporting scripture(s):

_____

_____

_____

Inspirational Scriptures

1 Thessalonians 5:16–18, Philippians 4:6–7, Psalm 46:1, Galatians 6:9, James 1:2–3, Psalm 4:8, 2 Timothy 1:7, Jeremiah 29:11, Matthew 11:28, Psalm 121, Proverbs 16:3, Psalms 1:1–3 , Philippians 4:19, Psalm 51:12

Morning Meditation

Date: _____

What will be your prayer target today?

- Church

- Spiritual Leaders

- Family

- Government (country, state, or city)

- Marketplace

- The Unreached

- Destruction of Strongholds

- Other: _____

_____

_____

_____

_____

Inspirational Scriptures

Isaiah 40:31, Matthew 19:26, Philippians 4:19, Romans 8:28, John 14:27, Psalms 27:14, Matthew 6:33, Joshua 1:9, Matthew 6:25–27, Psalm 118:24, Proverbs 3:5–6, James 1:19–20, Isaiah 54:17, Psalm 51:10

Evening Reflection

Date: _____

What did you experience today?

_____

_____

_____

_____

If it was a good or bad experience, what was your reaction?

_____

_____

_____

Is this reaction in accordance with a Christian example?

_____

If yes, give scripture(s) that have guided you to your reaction?

_____

_____

If no, how could you have reacted differently, and what scripture(s) have you turned to for guidance?

_____

_____

_____

Supporting scripture(s):

_____

_____

_____

Inspirational Scriptures

1 Thessalonians 5:16–18, Philippians 4:6–7, Psalm 46:1, Galatians 6:9, James 1:2–3, Psalm 4:8, 2 Timothy 1:7, Jeremiah 29:11, Matthew 11:28, Psalm 121, Proverbs 16:3, Psalms 1:1–3 , Philippians 4:19, Psalm 51:12

Accountability

Accountability Questionnaire

Romans 14:12, 1 Thessalonians 5:11, Colossians 3:16

Circle your answer.

Did you check your attitude today?

      Yes   No

Did you give to someone in need today?

      Yes   No

Did you help someone who was in need today?

      Yes   No

Did you give a kind word to someone or lend your ear to listen?

      Yes   No

Did you pray for someone today other than yourself?

      Yes   No

Were you a good steward today over the things that God has entrusted you with?

      Yes   No

Did you set any spiritual goals this week or attend any church activities?

      Yes   No

Have you put forth an effort to make your relationships better (friends, family, marriage)?

      Yes   No

MY FAITH, MY WALK

Did you control your tongue today?

       Yes   No

Have you been trustworthy?

       Yes   No

Did you overcome any impure urges today (sexual, smoking, gossiping, overeating)?

       Yes   No

Thoughts:

_____

_____

_____

_____

Accountability Questionnaire

Romans 14:12, 1 Thessalonians 5:11, Colossians 3:16

Circle your answer.

Did you check your attitude today?

Yes   No

Did you give to someone in need today?

Yes   No

Did you help someone who was in need today?

Yes   No

Did you give a kind word to someone or lend your ear to listen?

Yes   No

Did you pray for someone today other than yourself?

Yes   No

Were you a good steward today over the things that God has entrusted you with?

Yes   No

Did you set any spiritual goals this week or attend any church activities?

Yes   No

Have you put forth an effort to make your relationships better (friends, family, marriage)?

Yes   No

MY FAITH, MY WALK

Did you control your tongue today?

       Yes   No

Have you been trustworthy?

       Yes   No

Did you overcome any impure urges today (sexual, smoking, gossiping, overeating)?

       Yes   No

Thoughts:

_____

_____

_____

_____

Accountability Questionnaire

Romans 14:12, 1 Thessalonians 5:11, Colossians 3:16

Circle your answer.

Did you check your attitude today?

      Yes   No

Did you give to someone in need today?

      Yes   No

Did you help someone who was in need today?

      Yes   No

Did you give a kind word to someone or lend your ear to listen?

      Yes   No

Did you pray for someone today other than yourself?

      Yes   No

Were you a good steward today over the things that God has entrusted you with?

      Yes   No

Did you set any spiritual goals this week or attend any church activities?

      Yes   No

Have you put forth an effort to make your relationships better (friends, family, marriage)?

      Yes   No

Did you control your tongue today?

       Yes   No

Have you been trustworthy?

       Yes   No

Did you overcome any impure urges today (sexual, smoking, gossiping, overeating)?

       Yes   No

Thoughts:

_____

_____

_____

_____

Accountability Questionnaire

Romans 14:12, 1 Thessalonians 5:11, Colossians 3:16

Circle your answer.

Did you check your attitude today?

     Yes   No

Did you give to someone in need today?

     Yes   No

Did you help someone who was in need today?

     Yes   No

Did you give a kind word to someone or lend your ear to listen?

     Yes   No

Did you pray for someone today other than yourself?

     Yes   No

Were you a good steward today over the things that God has entrusted you with?

     Yes   No

Did you set any spiritual goals this week or attend any church activities?

     Yes   No

Have you put forth an effort to make your relationships better (friends, family, marriage)?

     Yes   No

My Faith, My Walk

Did you control your tongue today?

Yes   No

Have you been trustworthy?

Yes   No

Did you overcome any impure urges today (sexual, smoking, gossiping, overeating)?

Yes   No

Thoughts:

_____

_____

_____

_____

Accountability Questionnaire

Romans 14:12, 1 Thessalonians 5:11, Colossians 3:16

Circle your answer.

Did you check your attitude today?

       Yes   No

Did you give to someone in need today?

       Yes   No

Did you help someone who was in need today?

       Yes   No

Did you give a kind word to someone or lend your ear to listen?

       Yes   No

Did you pray for someone today other than yourself?

       Yes   No

Were you a good steward today over the things that God has entrusted you with?

       Yes   No

Did you set any spiritual goals this week or attend any church activities?

       Yes   No

Have you put forth an effort to make your relationships better (friends, family, marriage)?

       Yes   No

MY FAITH, MY WALK

Did you control your tongue today?

       Yes   No

Have you been trustworthy?

       Yes   No

Did you overcome any impure urges today (sexual, smoking, gossiping, overeating)?

       Yes   No

Thoughts:

_____

_____

_____

_____

Accountability Questionnaire

Romans 14:12, 1 Thessalonians 5:11, Colossians 3:16

Circle your answer.

Did you check your attitude today?

Yes   No

Did you give to someone in need today?

Yes   No

Did you help someone who was in need today?

Yes   No

Did you give a kind word to someone or lend your ear to listen?

Yes   No

Did you pray for someone today other than yourself?

Yes   No

Were you a good steward today over the things that God has entrusted you with?

Yes   No

Did you set any spiritual goals this week or attend any church activities?

Yes   No

Have you put forth an effort to make your relationships better (friends, family, marriage)?

Yes   No

MY FAITH, MY WALK

Did you control your tongue today? Yes No
Have you been trustworthy?

Yes No

Did you overcome any impure urges today (sexual, smoking, gossiping, overeating)?

Yes No

Thoughts:

_____

_____

_____

_____

Accountability Questionnaire

Romans 14:12, 1 Thessalonians 5:11, Colossians 3:16

Circle your answer.

Did you check your attitude today?

> Yes   No

Did you give to someone in need today?

> Yes   No

Did you help someone who was in need today?

> Yes   No

Did you give a kind word to someone or lend your ear to listen?

> Yes   No

Did you pray for someone today other than yourself?

> Yes   No

Were you a good steward today over the things that God has entrusted you with?

> Yes   No

Did you set any spiritual goals this week or attend any church activities?

> Yes   No

Have you put forth an effort to make your relationships better (friends, family, marriage)?

> Yes   No

MY FAITH, MY WALK

Did you control your tongue today?

Yes   No

Have you been trustworthy?

Yes   No

Did you overcome any impure urges today (sexual, smoking, gossiping, overeating)?

Yes   No

Thoughts:

_____

_____

_____

_____

Accountability Questionnaire

Romans 14:12, 1 Thessalonians 5:11, Colossians 3:16

Circle your answer.

Did you check your attitude today?

    Yes   No

Did you give to someone in need today?

    Yes   No

Did you help someone who was in need today?

    Yes   No

Did you give a kind word to someone or lend your ear to listen?

    Yes   No

Did you pray for someone today other than yourself?

    Yes   No

Were you a good steward today over the things that God has entrusted you with?

    Yes   No

Did you set any spiritual goals this week or attend any church activities?

    Yes   No

Have you put forth an effort to make your relationships better (friends, family, marriage)?

    Yes   No

Did you control your tongue today?

     Yes   No

Have you been trustworthy?

     Yes   No

Did you overcome any impure urges today (sexual, smoking, gossiping, overeating)?

     Yes   No

Thoughts:

_____

_____

_____

_____

Accountability Questionnaire

Romans 14:12, 1 Thessalonians 5:11, Colossians 3:16

Circle your answer.

Did you check your attitude today?

Yes   No

Did you give to someone in need today?

Yes   No

Did you help someone who was in need today?

Yes   No

Did you give a kind word to someone or lend your ear to listen?

Yes   No

Did you pray for someone today other than yourself?

Yes   No

Were you a good steward today over the things that God has entrusted you with?

Yes   No

Did you set any spiritual goals this week or attend any church activities?

Yes   No

Have you put forth an effort to make your relationships better (friends, family, marriage)?

Yes   No

MY FAITH, MY WALK

Did you control your tongue today?

Yes　　No

Have you been trustworthy?

Yes　　No

Did you overcome any impure urges today (sexual, smoking, gossiping, overeating)?

Yes　　No

Thoughts:

_____

_____

_____

_____

Accountability Questionnaire

Romans 14:12, 1 Thessalonians 5:11, Colossians 3:16

Circle your answer.

Did you check your attitude today?

Yes   No

Did you give to someone in need today?

Yes   No

Did you help someone who was in need today?

Yes   No

Did you give a kind word to someone or lend your ear to listen?

Yes   No

Did you pray for someone today other than yourself?

Yes   No

Were you a good steward today over the things that God has entrusted you with?

Yes   No

Did you set any spiritual goals this week or attend any church activities?

Yes   No

Have you put forth an effort to make your relationships better (friends, family, marriage)?

Yes   No

Did you control your tongue today?

      Yes   No

Have you been trustworthy?

      Yes   No

Did you overcome any impure urges today (sexual, smoking, gossiping, overeating)?

      Yes   No

Thoughts:

_____

_____

_____

_____

Accountability Questionnaire

Romans 14:12, 1 Thessalonians 5:11, Colossians 3:16

Circle your answer.

Did you check your attitude today?

       Yes   No

Did you give to someone in need today?

       Yes   No

Did you help someone who was in need today?

       Yes   No

Did you give a kind word to someone or lend your ear to listen?

       Yes   No

Did you pray for someone today other than yourself?

       Yes   No

Were you a good steward today over the things that God has entrusted you with?

       Yes   No

Did you set any spiritual goals this week or attend any church activities?

       Yes   No

Have you put forth an effort to make your relationships better (friends, family, marriage)?

       Yes   No

MY FAITH, MY WALK

Did you control your tongue today?

       Yes   No

Have you been trustworthy?

       Yes   No

Did you overcome any impure urges today (sexual, smoking, gossiping, overeating)?

       Yes   No

Thoughts:

_____

_____

_____

_____

Accountability Questionnaire

Romans 14:12, 1 Thessalonians 5:11, Colossians 3:16

Circle your answer.

Did you check your attitude today?

Yes   No

Did you give to someone in need today?

Yes   No

Did you help someone who was in need today?

Yes   No

Did you give a kind word to someone or lend your ear to listen?

Yes   No

Did you pray for someone today other than yourself?

Yes   No

Were you a good steward today over the things that God has entrusted you with?

Yes   No

Did you set any spiritual goals this week or attend any church activities?

Yes   No

Have you put forth an effort to make your relationships better (friends, family, marriage)?

Yes   No

Did you control your tongue today?

       Yes   No

Have you been trustworthy?

       Yes   No

Did you overcome any impure urges today (sexual, smoking, gossiping, overeating)?

       Yes   No

Thoughts:

_____

_____

_____

_____

Accountability Questionnaire

Romans 14:12, 1 Thessalonians 5:11, Colossians 3:16

Circle your answer.

Did you check your attitude today?

      Yes   No

Did you give to someone in need today?

      Yes   No

Did you help someone who was in need today?

      Yes   No

Did you give a kind word to someone or lend your ear to listen?

      Yes   No

Did you pray for someone today other than yourself?

      Yes   No

Were you a good steward today over the things that God has entrusted you with?

      Yes   No

Did you set any spiritual goals this week or attend any church activities?

      Yes   No

Have you put forth an effort to make your relationships better (friends, family, marriage)?

      Yes   No

MY FAITH, MY WALK

Did you control your tongue today?

      Yes   No

Have you been trustworthy?

      Yes   No

Did you overcome any impure urges today (sexual, smoking, gossiping, overeating)?

      Yes   No

Thoughts:

_____

_____

_____

_____

Accountability Questionnaire

Romans 14:12, 1 Thessalonians 5:11, Colossians 3:16

Circle your answer.

Did you check your attitude today?

      Yes   No

Did you give to someone in need today?

      Yes   No

Did you help someone who was in need today?

      Yes   No

Did you give a kind word to someone or lend your ear to listen?

      Yes   No

Did you pray for someone today other than yourself?

      Yes   No

Were you a good steward today over the things that God has entrusted you with?

      Yes   No

Did you set any spiritual goals this week or attend any church activities?

      Yes   No

Have you put forth an effort to make your relationships better (friends, family, marriage)?

      Yes   No

Did you control your tongue today?

>   Yes   No

Have you been trustworthy?

>   Yes   No

Did you overcome any impure urges today (sexual, smoking, gossiping, overeating)?

>   Yes   No

Fasting* and Praying

*Please consult a physician before fasting.

Fasting and Praying: Week 1

Matthew 6:16–18, 1 Corinthians 7:3–5

If you decide to fast, why did you decide to fast or what are you seeking from God?

_____

_____

_____

_____

What do you hope to accomplish or to take from this experience? Or what is your prayer?

_____

_____

_____

_____

What are you abstaining from?

_____

_____

How long are you fasting?

_____

_____

_____

What scriptures will you be referencing during this fast?

_____

_____

_____

Daily Journal

During your days of fasting and praying, document your day and what God has revealed to you.

_____

_____

_____

_____

_____

_____

_____

Fasting and Praying: Week 2

Matthew 6:16–18, 1 Corinthians 7:3–5

If you decide to fast, why did you decide to fast or what are you seeking from God?

_____

_____

_____

_____

What do you hope to accomplish or to take from this experience? Or what is your prayer?

_____

_____

_____

_____

What are you abstaining from?

_____

_____

How long are you fasting?

_____

_____

_____

MY FAITH, MY WALK

What scriptures will you be referencing during this fast?

_____

_____

_____

Daily Journal

During your days of fasting and praying, document your day and what God has revealed to you.

_____

_____

_____

_____

_____

_____

_____

Fasting and Praying: Week 3

Matthew 6:16–18, 1 Corinthians 7:3–5

If you decide to fast, why did you decide to fast or what are you seeking from God?

_____

_____

_____

_____

What do you hope to accomplish or to take from this experience? Or what is your prayer?

_____

_____

_____

_____

What are you abstaining from?

_____

_____

How long are you fasting?

_____

_____

_____

What scriptures will you be referencing during this fast?

_____

_____

_____

Daily Journal

During your days of fasting and praying, document your day and what God has revealed to you.

_____

_____

_____

_____

_____

_____

_____

Fasting and Praying: Week 4

Matthew 6:16–18, 1 Corinthians 7:3–5

If you decide to fast, why did you decide to fast or what are you seeking from God?

_____

_____

_____

_____

What do you hope to accomplish or to take from this experience? Or what is your prayer?

_____

_____

_____

_____

What are you abstaining from?

_____

_____

How long are you fasting?

_____

_____

_____

What scriptures will you be referencing during this fast?

_____

_____

_____

Daily Journal

During your days of fasting and praying, document your day and what God has revealed to you.

_____

_____

_____

_____

_____

_____

_____

Fasting and Praying: Week 5

Matthew 6:16–18, 1 Corinthians 7:3–5

If you decide to fast, why did you decide to fast or what are you seeking from God?

_____

_____

_____

_____

What do you hope to accomplish or to take from this experience? Or what is your prayer?

_____

_____

_____

_____

What are you abstaining from?

_____

_____

How long are you fasting?

_____

_____

_____

What scriptures will you be referencing during this fast?

_____

_____

_____

Daily Journal

During your days of fasting and praying, document your day and what God has revealed to you.

_____

_____

_____

_____

_____

_____

_____

Fasting and Praying: Week 6

Matthew 6:16–18, 1 Corinthians 7:3–5

If you decide to fast, why did you decide to fast or what are you seeking from God?

_____

_____

_____

_____

What do you hope to accomplish or to take from this experience? Or what is your prayer?

_____

_____

_____

_____

What are you abstaining from?

_____

_____

How long are you fasting?

_____

_____

_____

What scriptures will you be referencing during this fast?

_____

_____

_____

Daily Journal

During your days of fasting and praying, document your day and what God has revealed to you.

_____

_____

_____

_____

_____

_____

_____

_____

Fasting and Praying: Week 7

Matthew 6:16–18, 1 Corinthians 7:3–5

If you decide to fast, why did you decide to fast or what are you seeking from God?

_____

_____

_____

_____

What do you hope to accomplish or to take from this experience? Or what is your prayer?

_____

_____

_____

_____

What are you abstaining from?

_____

_____

How long are you fasting?

_____

_____

_____

What scriptures will you be referencing during this fast?

_____

_____

_____

Daily Journal

During your days of fasting and praying, document your day and what God has revealed to you.

_____

_____

_____

_____

_____

_____

_____

_____

Time, Tithes, and Offerings

Time

Matthew 6:33, 1 Peter 2:2, Romans 10:17

How much time did you give God today (in ministries, in prayer, in worship, in praise, personal talks, or meditation)?

15 mins ☐   30 mins ☐   1hr ☐   2hrs ☐   Other:_____

(If you have spent time in increments throughout the day, you can add it up at the end of the day.)

Tithes and Offerings

Malachi 3:10

Date:_____   Date:_____
Tithes: $_____   Tithes: $_____
Offerings: $_____   Offerings: $_____
Other: $_____   Other: $_____
Total: $_____   Total: $_____

(Other Contributions)

Charity Participation: _____

    Hrs. _____   Charity Donation: $ _____

Charity Participation: _____

    Hrs. _____   Charity Donation: $ _____

Charity Participation: _____

    Hrs. _____   Charity Donation: $ _____

Time

Matthew 6:33, 1 Peter 2:2, Romans 10:17

How much time did you give God today (in ministries, in prayer, in worship, in praise, personal talks, or meditation)?

15 mins ☐   30 mins ☐   1hr ☐   2hrs ☐   Other:_____

(If you have spent time in increments throughout the day, you can add it up at the end of the day.)

Tithes and Offerings

Malachi 3:10

Date:_____   Date:_____
Tithes: $_____   Tithes: $_____
Offerings: $_____   Offerings: $_____
Other: $_____   Other: $_____
Total: $_____   Total: $_____

(Other Contributions)

Charity Participation: _____
        Hrs. _____   Charity Donation: $ _____
Charity Participation: _____
        Hrs. _____   Charity Donation: $ _____
Charity Participation: _____
        Hrs. _____   Charity Donation: $ _____

Time

Matthew 6:33, 1 Peter 2:2, Romans 10:17

How much time did you give God today (in ministries, in prayer, in worship, in praise, personal talks, or meditation)?

15 mins ☐   30 mins ☐   1hr ☐   2hrs ☐   Other:_____

(If you have spent time in increments throughout the day, you can add it up at the end of the day.)

Tithes and Offerings

Malachi 3:10

Date:_____   Date:_____
Tithes: $_____   Tithes: $_____
Offerings: $_____   Offerings: $_____
Other: $_____   Other: $_____
Total: $_____   Total: $_____

(Other Contributions)

Charity Participation: _____
        Hrs. _____   Charity Donation: $ _____
Charity Participation: _____
        Hrs. _____   Charity Donation: $ _____
Charity Participation: _____
        Hrs. _____   Charity Donation: $ _____

Time

Matthew 6:33, 1 Peter 2:2, Romans 10:17

How much time did you give God today (in ministries, in prayer, in worship, in praise, personal talks, or meditation)?

15 mins ☐   30 mins ☐   1hr ☐   2hrs ☐   Other:_____

(If you have spent time in increments throughout the day, you can add it up at the end of the day.)

Tithes and Offerings

Malachi 3:10

Date:_____   Date:_____
Tithes: $_____   Tithes: $_____
Offerings: $_____   Offerings: $_____
Other: $_____   Other: $_____
Total: $_____   Total: $_____

(Other Contributions)

Charity Participation: _____

　　　Hrs. _____   Charity Donation: $ _____

Charity Participation: _____

　　　Hrs. _____   Charity Donation: $ _____

Charity Participation: _____

　　　Hrs. _____   Charity Donation: $ _____

Time

Matthew 6:33, 1 Peter 2:2, Romans 10:17

How much time did you give God today (in ministries, in prayer, in worship, in praise, personal talks, or meditation)?

15 mins ☐   30 mins ☐   1hr ☐   2hrs ☐   Other:_____

(If you have spent time in increments throughout the day, you can add it up at the end of the day.)

Tithes and Offerings

Malachi 3:10

Date:_____   Date:_____
Tithes: $_____   Tithes: $_____
Offerings: $_____   Offerings: $_____
Other: $_____   Other: $_____
Total: $_____   Total: $_____

(Other Contributions)

Charity Participation: _____
    Hrs. _____   Charity Donation: $ _____
Charity Participation: _____
    Hrs. _____   Charity Donation: $ _____
Charity Participation: _____
    Hrs. _____   Charity Donation: $ _____

Time

Matthew 6:33, 1 Peter 2:2, Romans 10:17

How much time did you give God today (in ministries, in prayer, in worship, in praise, personal talks, or meditation)?

15 mins ☐   30 mins ☐   1hr ☐   2hrs ☐   Other:_____

(If you have spent time in increments throughout the day, you can add it up at the end of the day.)

Tithes and Offerings

Malachi 3:10

Date:_____   Date:_____
Tithes: $_____   Tithes: $_____
Offerings: $_____   Offerings: $_____
Other: $_____   Other: $_____
Total: $_____   Total: $_____

(Other Contributions)

Charity Participation: _____

      Hrs. _____   Charity Donation: $ _____

Charity Participation: _____

      Hrs. _____   Charity Donation: $ _____

Charity Participation: _____

      Hrs. _____   Charity Donation: $ _____

Time

Matthew 6:33, 1 Peter 2:2, Romans 10:17

How much time did you give God today (in ministries, in prayer, in worship, in praise, personal talks, or meditation)?

15 mins ☐   30 mins ☐   1hr ☐   2hrs ☐   Other:_____

(If you have spent time in increments throughout the day, you can add it up at the end of the day.)

Tithes and Offerings

Malachi 3:10

Date:_____   Date:_____
Tithes: $_____   Tithes: $_____
Offerings: $_____   Offerings: $_____
Other: $_____   Other: $_____
Total: $_____   Total: $_____

(Other Contributions)

Charity Participation: _____
          Hrs. _____   Charity Donation: $ _____
Charity Participation: _____
          Hrs. _____   Charity Donation: $ _____
Charity Participation: _____
          Hrs. _____   Charity Donation: $ _____

Time

Matthew 6:33, 1 Peter 2:2, Romans 10:17

How much time did you give God today (in ministries, in prayer, in worship, in praise, personal talks, or meditation)?

15 mins ☐   30 mins ☐   1hr ☐   2hrs ☐   Other:_____

(If you have spent time in increments throughout the day, you can add it up at the end of the day.)

Tithes and Offerings

Malachi 3:10

Date:_____   Date:_____
Tithes: $_____   Tithes: $_____
Offerings: $_____   Offerings: $_____
Other: $_____   Other: $_____
Total: $_____   Total: $_____

(Other Contributions)

Charity Participation: _____

    Hrs. _____   Charity Donation: $ _____

Charity Participation: _____

    Hrs. _____   Charity Donation: $ _____

Charity Participation: _____

    Hrs. _____   Charity Donation: $ _____

Time

Matthew 6:33, 1 Peter 2:2, Romans 10:17

How much time did you give God today (in ministries, in prayer, in worship, in praise, personal talks, or meditation)?

15 mins ☐   30 mins ☐   1hr ☐   2hrs ☐   Other:_____

(If you have spent time in increments throughout the day, you can add it up at the end of the day.)

Tithes and Offerings

Malachi 3:10

Date:_____   Date:_____
Tithes: $_____   Tithes: $_____
Offerings: $_____   Offerings: $_____
Other: $_____   Other: $_____
Total: $_____   Total: $_____

(Other Contributions)

Charity Participation: _____

      Hrs. _____   Charity Donation: $ _____

Charity Participation: _____

      Hrs. _____   Charity Donation: $ _____

Charity Participation: _____

      Hrs. _____   Charity Donation: $ _____

Time

Matthew 6:33, 1 Peter 2:2, Romans 10:17

How much time did you give God today (in ministries, in prayer, in worship, in praise, personal talks, or meditation)?

15 mins ☐   30 mins ☐   1hr ☐   2hrs ☐   Other:_____

(If you have spent time in increments throughout the day, you can add it up at the end of the day.)

Tithes and Offerings

Malachi 3:10

Date:_____   Date:_____
Tithes: $_____   Tithes: $_____
Offerings: $_____   Offerings: $_____
Other: $_____   Other: $_____
Total: $_____   Total: $_____

(Other Contributions)

Charity Participation: _____
        Hrs. _____   Charity Donation: $ _____
Charity Participation: _____
        Hrs. _____   Charity Donation: $ _____
Charity Participation: _____
        Hrs. _____   Charity Donation: $ _____

Time

Matthew 6:33, 1 Peter 2:2, Romans 10:17

How much time did you give God today (in ministries, in prayer, in worship, in praise, personal talks, or meditation)?

15 mins ☐   30 mins ☐   1hr ☐   2hrs ☐   Other:_____

(If you have spent time in increments throughout the day, you can add it up at the end of the day.)

Tithes and Offerings

Malachi 3:10

Date:_____   Date:_____
Tithes: $_____   Tithes: $_____
Offerings: $_____   Offerings: $_____
Other: $_____   Other: $_____
Total: $_____   Total: $_____

(Other Contributions)

Charity Participation: _____
         Hrs. _____   Charity Donation: $ _____
Charity Participation: _____
         Hrs. _____   Charity Donation: $ _____
Charity Participation: _____
         Hrs. _____   Charity Donation: $ _____

Time

Matthew 6:33, 1 Peter 2:2, Romans 10:17

How much time did you give God today (in ministries, in prayer, in worship, in praise, personal talks, or meditation)?

15 mins ☐   30 mins ☐   1hr ☐   2hrs ☐   Other:_____

(If you have spent time in increments throughout the day, you can add it up at the end of the day.)

Tithes and Offerings

Malachi 3:10

Date:_____   Date:_____
Tithes: $_____   Tithes: $_____
Offerings: $_____   Offerings: $_____
Other: $_____   Other: $_____
Total: $_____   Total: $_____

(Other Contributions)

Charity Participation: _____
      Hrs. _____   Charity Donation: $_____
Charity Participation: _____
      Hrs. _____   Charity Donation: $_____
Charity Participation: _____
      Hrs. _____   Charity Donation: $_____

Bible Study Notes

Bible Study Notes

Date: _____

Place: _____

Delivered by: _____

Topic: _____

Sources: _____

_____

_____

_____

Scriptures: _____

_____

_____

_____

Key Points/Steps: _____

_____

_____

_____

_____

Notes:

_____

_____

_____

MY FAITH, MY WALK

Bible Study Notes

Date: _____

Place: _____

Delivered by: _____

Topic: _____

Sources: _____

_____

_____

_____

Scriptures: _____

_____

_____

_____

Key Points/Steps: _____

_____

_____

_____

_____

Notes:

_____

_____

_____

My Faith, My Walk

Bible Study Notes

Date: _____

Place: _____

Delivered by: _____

Topic: _____

Sources: _____

_____

_____

_____

Scriptures: _____

_____

_____

_____

Key Points/Steps: _____

_____

_____

_____

_____

Notes:

_____

_____

_____

My Faith, My Walk

Bible Study Notes

Date: _____

Place: _____

Delivered by: _____

Topic: _____

Sources: _____

_____

_____

_____

Scriptures: _____

_____

_____

_____

Key Points/Steps: _____

_____

_____

_____

_____

Notes:

_____

_____

_____

My Faith, My Walk

Bible Study Notes

Date: _____

Place: _____

Delivered by: _____

Topic: _____

Sources: _____

_____

_____

_____

Scriptures: _____

_____

_____

_____

Key Points/Steps: _____

_____

_____

_____

_____

Notes:

_____

_____

_____

MY FAITH, MY WALK

Bible Study Notes

Date: _____

Place: _____

Delivered by: _____

Topic: _____

Sources: _____

_____

_____

_____

Scriptures: _____

_____

_____

_____

Key Points/Steps: _____

_____

_____

_____

_____

Notes:

_____

_____

_____

My Faith, My Walk

Bible Study Notes

Date: _____

Place: _____

Delivered by: _____

Topic: _____

Sources: _____

_____

_____

_____

Scriptures: _____

_____

_____

_____

Key Points/Steps: _____

_____

_____

_____

_____

Notes:

_____

_____

_____

MY FAITH, MY WALK

_____

_____

_____

_____

_____

_____

_____

_____

_____

_____

_____

_____

_____

_____

_____

_____

_____

_____

_____

_____

_____

_____

Bible Study Notes

Date: _____

Place: _____

Delivered by: _____

Topic: _____

Sources: _____

_____

_____

_____

Scriptures: _____

_____

_____

_____

Key Points/Steps: _____

_____

_____

_____

_____

Notes:

_____

_____

_____

My Faith, My Walk

Bible Study Notes

Date: _____

Place: _____

Delivered by: _____

Topic: _____

Sources: _____

_____

_____

_____

Scriptures: _____

_____

_____

_____

Key Points/Steps: _____

_____

_____

_____

_____

Notes:

_____

_____

_____

Bible Study Notes

Date: _____

Place: _____

Delivered by: _____

Topic: _____

Sources: _____

_____

_____

_____

Scriptures: _____

_____

_____

_____

Key Points/Steps: _____

_____

_____

_____

_____

Notes:

_____

_____

_____

My Faith, My Walk

Bible Study Notes

Date: _____

Place: _____

Delivered by: _____

Topic: _____

Sources: _____

_____

_____

_____

Scriptures: _____

_____

_____

_____

Key Points/Steps: _____

_____

_____

_____

_____

Notes:

_____

_____

_____

My Faith, My Walk

Bible Study Notes

Date: _____

Place: _____

Delivered by: _____

Topic: _____

Sources: _____

_____

_____

_____

Scriptures: _____

_____

_____

_____

Key Points/Steps: _____

_____

_____

_____

_____

Notes:

_____

_____

_____

My Faith, My Walk

Bible Study Notes

Date: _____

Place: _____

Delivered by: _____

Topic: _____

Sources: _____

_____

_____

_____

Scriptures: _____

_____

_____

_____

Key Points/Steps: _____

_____

_____

_____

_____

Notes:

_____

_____

_____

My Faith, My Walk

Bible Study Notes

Date: _____

Place: _____

Delivered by: _____

Topic: _____

Sources: _____

_____

_____

_____

Scriptures: _____

_____

_____

_____

Key Points/Steps: _____

_____

_____

_____

_____

Notes:

_____

_____

_____

My Faith, My Walk

Bible Study Notes

Date: _____

Place: _____

Delivered by: _____

Topic: _____

Sources: _____

_____

_____

_____

Scriptures: _____

_____

_____

_____

Key Points/Steps: _____

_____

_____

_____

_____

Notes:

_____

_____

_____

My Faith, My Walk

Bible Study Notes

Date: _____

Place: _____

Delivered by: _____

Topic: _____

Sources: _____

_____

_____

_____

Scriptures: _____

_____

_____

_____

Key Points/Steps: _____

_____

_____

_____

_____

Notes:

_____

_____

_____

MY FAITH, MY WALK

Bible Study Notes

Date: _____

Place: _____

Delivered by: _____

Topic: _____

Sources: _____

_____

_____

_____

Scriptures: _____

_____

_____

_____

Key Points/Steps: _____

_____

_____

_____

_____

Notes:

_____

_____

_____

My Faith, My Walk

Bible Study Notes

Date: _____

Place: _____

Delivered by: _____

Topic: _____

Sources: _____

_____

_____

_____

Scriptures: _____

_____

_____

_____

Key Points/Steps: _____

_____

_____

_____

_____

Notes:

_____

_____

_____

Bible Study Notes

Date: _____

Place: _____

Delivered by: _____

Topic: _____

Sources: _____

_____

_____

_____

Scriptures: _____

_____

_____

_____

Key Points/Steps: _____

_____

_____

_____

_____

Notes:

_____

_____

_____

My Faith, My Walk

Bible Study Notes

Date: _____

Place: _____

Delivered by: _____

Topic: _____

Sources: _____

_____

_____

_____

Scriptures: _____

_____

_____

_____

Key Points/Steps: _____

_____

_____

_____

Notes:

_____

_____

_____

My Faith, My Walk

Bible Study Notes

Date: _____

Place: _____

Delivered by: _____

Topic: _____

Sources: _____

_____

_____

_____

Scriptures: _____

_____

_____

_____

Key Points/Steps: _____

_____

_____

_____

_____

Notes:

_____

_____

_____

MY FAITH, MY WALK

Bible Study Notes

Date: _____

Place: _____

Delivered by: _____

Topic: _____

Sources: _____

_____

_____

_____

Scriptures: _____

_____

_____

_____

Key Points/Steps: _____

_____

_____

_____

_____

Notes:

_____

_____

_____

My Faith, My Walk

Bible Study Notes

Date: _____

Place: _____

Delivered by: _____

Topic: _____

Sources: _____

_____

_____

_____

Scriptures: _____

_____

_____

_____

Key Points/Steps: _____

_____

_____

_____

_____

Notes:

_____

_____

_____

My Faith, My Walk

Bible Study Notes

Date: _____

Place: _____

Delivered by: _____

Topic: _____

Sources: _____

_____

_____

_____

Scriptures: _____

_____

_____

_____

Key Points/Steps: _____

_____

_____

_____

_____

Notes:

_____

_____

_____

MY FAITH, MY WALK

Bible Study Notes

Date: _____

Place: _____

Delivered by: _____

Topic: _____

Sources: _____

_____

_____

_____

Scriptures: _____

_____

_____

_____

Key Points/Steps: _____

_____

_____

_____

_____

Notes:

_____

_____

_____

My Faith, My Walk

Bible Study Notes

Date: _____

Place: _____

Delivered by: _____

Topic: _____

Sources: _____

_____

_____

_____

Scriptures: _____

_____

_____

_____

Key Points/Steps: _____

_____

_____

_____

_____

Notes:

_____

_____

_____

My Faith, My Walk

Bible Study Notes

Date: _____

Place: _____

Delivered by: _____

Topic: _____

Sources: _____

_____

_____

_____

Scriptures: _____

_____

_____

Key Points/Steps: _____

_____

_____

_____

Notes:

_____

_____

_____

My Faith, My Walk

Bible Study Notes

Date: _____

Place: _____

Delivered by: _____

Topic: _____

Sources: _____

_____

_____

_____

Scriptures: _____

_____

_____

_____

Key Points/Steps: _____

_____

_____

_____

_____

Notes:

_____

_____

_____

MY FAITH, MY WALK

Bible Study Notes

Date: _____

Place: _____

Delivered by: _____

Topic: _____

Sources: _____

_____

_____

_____

Scriptures: _____

_____

_____

_____

Key Points/Steps: _____

_____

_____

_____

_____

Notes:

_____

_____

_____

My Faith, My Walk

Bible Study Notes

Date: _____

Place: _____

Delivered by: _____

Topic: _____

Sources: _____

_____

_____

_____

Scriptures: _____

_____

_____

_____

Key Points/Steps: _____

_____

_____

_____

_____

Notes:

_____

_____

_____

My Faith, My Walk

Sermon Notes

Sermon Notes

Date: _____

Place: _____

Delivered by: _____

Topic: _____

Sources: _____

_____

_____

_____

Scriptures: _____

_____

_____

_____

Key Points/Steps: _____

_____

_____

_____

_____

Notes:

_____

_____

_____

_____

MY FAITH, MY WALK

_____

_____

_____

_____

_____

_____

_____

_____

_____

_____

List the things you are learning about who you are in Christ and the kingdom.

_____

_____

_____

_____

What is your perspective of God today?

_____

_____

_____

Sermon Notes

Date: _____

Place: _____

Delivered by: _____

Topic: _____

Sources: _____

_____

_____

_____

Scriptures: _____

_____

_____

_____

Key Points/Steps: _____

_____

_____

_____

Notes:

_____

_____

_____

_____

_____

_____

_____

_____

_____

_____

_____

_____

_____

_____

List the things you are learning about who you are in Christ and the kingdom.

_____

_____

_____

What is your perspective of God today?

_____

_____

_____

Sermon Notes

Date: _____

Place: _____

Delivered by: _____

Topic: _____

Sources: _____

_____

_____

_____

Scriptures: _____

_____

_____

_____

Key Points/Steps: _____

_____

_____

_____

Notes:

_____

_____

_____

_____

MY FAITH, MY WALK

_____

_____

_____

_____

_____

_____

_____

_____

_____

List the things you are learning about who you are in Christ and the kingdom.

_____

_____

_____

What is your perspective of God today?

_____

_____

_____

Sermon Notes

Date: _____

Place: _____

Delivered by: _____

Topic: _____

Sources: _____

_____

_____

_____

Scriptures: _____

_____

_____

_____

Key Points/Steps: _____

_____

_____

_____

_____

Notes:

_____

_____

_____

_____

_____

_____

_____

_____

_____

_____

_____

_____

_____

_____

List the things you are learning about who you are in Christ and the kingdom.

_____

_____

_____

What is your perspective of God today?

_____

_____

_____

Sermon Notes

Date: _____

Place: _____

Delivered by: _____

Topic: _____

Sources: _____

_____

_____

_____

Scriptures: _____

_____

_____

_____

Key Points/Steps: _____

_____

_____

_____

Notes:

_____

_____

_____

_____

MY FAITH, MY WALK

_____

_____

_____

_____

_____

_____

_____

_____

_____

_____

_____

List the things you are learning about who you are in Christ and the kingdom.

_____

_____

_____

What is your perspective of God today?

_____

_____

_____

Sermon Notes

Date: _____

Place: _____

Delivered by: _____

Topic: _____

Sources: _____

_____

_____

_____

Scriptures: _____

_____

_____

_____

Key Points/Steps: _____

_____

_____

_____

_____

Notes:

_____

_____

_____

_____

My Faith, My Walk

_____

_____

_____

_____

_____

_____

_____

_____

_____

_____

List the things you are learning about who you are in Christ and the kingdom.

_____

_____

_____

_____

What is your perspective of God today?

_____

_____

_____

Sermon Notes

Date: _____

Place: _____

Delivered by: _____

Topic: _____

Sources: _____

_____

_____

_____

Scriptures: _____

_____

_____

_____

Key Points/Steps: _____

_____

_____

_____

Notes:

_____

_____

_____

_____

_____

_____

_____

_____

_____

_____

_____

_____

_____

_____

_____

_____

List the things you are learning about who you are in Christ and the kingdom.

_____

_____

_____

_____

What is your perspective of God today?

_____

_____

_____

Sermon Notes

Date: _____

Place: _____

Delivered by: _____

Topic: _____

Sources: _____

_____

_____

_____

Scriptures: _____

_____

_____

_____

Key Points/Steps: _____

_____

_____

_____

_____

Notes:

_____

_____

_____

_____

_____

_____

_____

_____

_____

_____

_____

_____

_____

_____

_____

List the things you are learning about who you are in Christ and the kingdom.

_____

_____

_____

_____

What is your perspective of God today?

_____

_____

_____

Sermon Notes

Date: _____

Place: _____

Delivered by: _____

Topic: _____

Sources: _____

_____

_____

_____

Scriptures: _____

_____

_____

_____

Key Points/Steps: _____

_____

_____

_____

Notes:

_____

_____

_____

_____

_____

_____

_____

_____

_____

_____

_____

_____

_____

_____

_____

List the things you are learning about who you are in Christ and the kingdom.

_____

_____

_____

_____

What is your perspective of God today?

_____

_____

_____

Sermon Notes

Date: _____

Place: _____

Delivered by: _____

Topic: _____

Sources: _____

_____

_____

_____

Scriptures: _____

_____

_____

_____

Key Points/Steps: _____

_____

_____

_____

Notes:

_____

_____

_____

_____

My Faith, My Walk

_____

_____

_____

_____

_____

_____

_____

_____

_____

_____

_____

List the things you are learning about who you are in Christ and the kingdom.

_____

_____

_____

_____

What is your perspective of God today?

_____

_____

_____

Sermon Notes

Date: _____

Place: _____

Delivered by: _____

Topic: _____

Sources: _____

_____

_____

_____

Scriptures: _____

_____

_____

_____

Key Points/Steps: _____

_____

_____

_____

_____

Notes:

_____

_____

_____

_____

_____

_____

_____

_____

_____

_____

_____

_____

_____

_____

_____

List the things you are learning about who you are in Christ and the kingdom.

_____

_____

_____

_____

What is your perspective of God today?

_____

_____

_____

Sermon Notes

Date: _____

Place: _____

Delivered by: _____

Topic: _____

Sources: _____

_____

_____

_____

Scriptures: _____

_____

_____

_____

Key Points/Steps: _____

_____

_____

_____

_____

Notes:

_____

_____

_____

_____

_____

_____

_____

_____

_____

_____

_____

_____

_____

_____

List the things you are learning about who you are in Christ and the kingdom.

_____

_____

_____

_____

What is your perspective of God today?

_____

_____

_____

Sermon Notes

Date: _____

Place: _____

Delivered by: _____

Topic: _____

Sources: _____

_____

_____

_____

Scriptures: _____

_____

_____

_____

Key Points/Steps: _____

_____

_____

_____

Notes:

_____

_____

_____

_____

_____

_____

_____

_____

_____

_____

_____

_____

_____

_____

List the things you are learning about who you are in Christ and the kingdom.

_____

_____

_____

What is your perspective of God today?

_____

_____

_____

Sermon Notes

Date: _____

Place: _____

Delivered by: _____

Topic: _____

Sources: _____

_____

_____

_____

Scriptures: _____

_____

_____

_____

Key Points/Steps: _____

_____

_____

_____

_____

Notes:

_____

_____

_____

_____

_____

_____

_____

_____

_____

_____

_____

_____

_____

_____

List the things you are learning about who you are in Christ and the kingdom.

_____

_____

_____

_____

What is your perspective of God today?

_____

_____

_____

Sermon Notes

Date: _____

Place: _____

Delivered by: _____

Topic: _____

Sources: _____

_____

_____

_____

Scriptures: _____

_____

_____

_____

Key Points/Steps: _____

_____

_____

_____

Notes:

_____

_____

_____

_____

MY FAITH, MY WALK

_____

_____

_____

_____

_____

_____

_____

_____

_____

_____

_____

List the things you are learning about who you are in Christ and the kingdom.

_____

_____

_____

_____

What is your perspective of God today?

_____

_____

_____

Sermon Notes

Date: _____

Place: _____

Delivered by: _____

Topic: _____

Sources: _____

_____

_____

_____

Scriptures: _____

_____

_____

_____

Key Points/Steps: _____

_____

_____

_____

_____

Notes:

_____

_____

_____

_____

MY FAITH, MY WALK

_____

_____

_____

_____

_____

_____

_____

_____

_____

_____

List the things you are learning about who you are in Christ and the kingdom.

_____

_____

_____

What is your perspective of God today?

_____

_____

_____

Sermon Notes

Date: _____

Place: _____

Delivered by: _____

Topic: _____

Sources: _____

_____

_____

_____

Scriptures: _____

_____

_____

_____

Key Points/Steps: _____

_____

_____

_____

_____

Notes:

_____

_____

_____

_____

MY FAITH, MY WALK

_____

_____

_____

_____

_____

_____

_____

_____

_____

_____

_____

_____

List the things you are learning about who you are in Christ and the kingdom.

_____

_____

_____

_____

What is your perspective of God today?

_____

_____

_____

Sermon Notes

Date: _____

Place: _____

Delivered by: _____

Topic: _____

Sources: _____

_____

_____

_____

Scriptures: _____

_____

_____

_____

Key Points/Steps: _____

_____

_____

_____

_____

Notes:

_____

_____

_____

_____

MY FAITH, MY WALK

_____

_____

_____

_____

_____

_____

_____

_____

_____

_____

List the things you are learning about who you are in Christ and the kingdom.

_____

_____

_____

_____

What is your perspective of God today?

_____

_____

_____

Sermon Notes

Date: _____

Place: _____

Delivered by: _____

Topic: _____

Sources: _____

_____

_____

_____

Scriptures: _____

_____

_____

_____

Key Points/Steps: _____

_____

_____

_____

_____

Notes:

_____

_____

_____

_____

_____

_____

_____

_____

_____

_____

_____

_____

_____

_____

List the things you are learning about who you are in Christ and the kingdom.

_____

_____

_____

What is your perspective of God today?

_____

_____

_____

Sermon Notes

Date: _____

Place: _____

Delivered by: _____

Topic: _____

Sources: _____

_____

_____

_____

Scriptures: _____

_____

_____

_____

Key Points/Steps: _____

_____

_____

_____

_____

Notes:

_____

_____

_____

_____

_____

My Faith, My Walk

_____

_____

_____

_____

_____

_____

_____

_____

_____

_____

List the things you are learning about who you are in Christ and the kingdom.

_____

_____

_____

What is your perspective of God today?

_____

_____

_____

Sermon Notes

Date: _____

Place: _____

Delivered by: _____

Topic: _____

Sources: _____

_____

_____

_____

Scriptures: _____

_____

_____

_____

Key Points/Steps: _____

_____

_____

_____

_____

Notes:

_____

_____

_____

_____

List the things you are learning about who you are in Christ and the kingdom.

What is your perspective of God today?

Sermon Notes

Date: _____

Place: _____

Delivered by: _____

Topic: _____

Sources: _____

_____

_____

_____

Scriptures: _____

_____

_____

_____

Key Points/Steps: _____

_____

_____

_____

_____

Notes:

_____

_____

_____

_____

MY FAITH, MY WALK

_____

_____

_____

_____

_____

_____

_____

_____

_____

_____

List the things you are learning about who you are in Christ and the kingdom.

_____

_____

_____

_____

What is your perspective of God today?

_____

_____

_____

Sermon Notes

Date: _____

Place: _____

Delivered by: _____

Topic: _____

Sources: _____

_____

_____

_____

Scriptures: _____

_____

_____

_____

Key Points/Steps: _____

_____

_____

_____

Notes:

_____

_____

_____

_____

My Faith, My Walk

_____

_____

_____

_____

_____

_____

_____

_____

_____

_____

List the things you are learning about who you are in Christ and the kingdom.

_____

_____

_____

_____

What is your perspective of God today?

_____

_____

_____

Sermon Notes

Date: _____

Place: _____

Delivered by: _____

Topic: _____

Sources: _____

_____

_____

_____

Scriptures: _____

_____

_____

_____

Key Points/Steps: _____

_____

_____

_____

Notes:

_____

_____

_____

_____

MY FAITH, MY WALK

_____

_____

_____

_____

_____

_____

_____

_____

_____

_____

List the things you are learning about who you are in Christ and the kingdom.

_____

_____

_____

What is your perspective of God today?

_____

_____

_____

Sermon Notes

Date: _____

Place: _____

Delivered by: _____

Topic: _____

Sources: _____

_____

_____

_____

Scriptures: _____

_____

_____

_____

Key Points/Steps: _____

_____

_____

_____

_____

Notes:

_____

_____

_____

_____

_____

_____

_____

_____

_____

_____

_____

_____

_____

_____

_____

List the things you are learning about who you are in Christ and the kingdom.

_____

_____

_____

What is your perspective of God today?

_____

_____

_____

Sermon Notes

Date: _____

Place: _____

Delivered by: _____

Topic: _____

Sources: _____

_____

_____

_____

Scriptures: _____

_____

_____

_____

Key Points/Steps: _____

_____

_____

_____

_____

Notes:

_____

_____

_____

_____

MY FAITH, MY WALK

_____

_____

_____

_____

_____

_____

_____

_____

_____

_____

List the things you are learning about who you are in Christ and the kingdom.

_____

_____

_____

What is your perspective of God today?

_____

_____

_____

Sermon Notes

Date: _____

Place: _____

Delivered by: _____

Topic: _____

Sources: _____

_____

_____

_____

Scriptures: _____

_____

_____

_____

Key Points/Steps: _____

_____

_____

_____

Notes:

_____

_____

_____

_____

_____

_____

_____

_____

_____

_____

_____

_____

_____

_____

List the things you are learning about who you are in Christ and the kingdom.

_____

_____

_____

What is your perspective of God today?

_____

_____

_____

Sermon Notes

Date: _____

Place: _____

Delivered by: _____

Topic: _____

Sources: _____

_____

_____

_____

Scriptures: _____

_____

_____

_____

Key Points/Steps: _____

_____

_____

_____

Notes:

_____

_____

_____

_____

MY FAITH, MY WALK

_____

_____

_____

_____

_____

_____

_____

_____

_____

_____

List the things you are learning about who you are in Christ and the kingdom.

_____

_____

_____

_____

What is your perspective of God today?

_____

_____

_____

Sermon Notes

Date: _____

Place: _____

Delivered by: _____

Topic: _____

Sources: _____

_____

_____

_____

Scriptures: _____

_____

_____

_____

Key Points/Steps: _____

_____

_____

_____

_____

Notes:

_____

_____

_____

_____

_____

_____

_____

_____

_____

_____

_____

_____

_____

_____

_____

List the things you are learning about who you are in Christ and the kingdom.

_____

_____

_____

_____

What is your perspective of God today?

_____

_____

_____

Sermon Notes

Date: _____

Place: _____

Delivered by: _____

Topic: _____

Sources: _____

_____

_____

_____

Scriptures: _____

_____

_____

_____

Key Points/Steps: _____

_____

_____

_____

Notes:

_____

_____

_____

_____

My Faith, My Walk

_____

_____

_____

_____

_____

_____

_____

_____

_____

_____

List the things you are learning about who you are in Christ and the kingdom.

_____

_____

_____

_____

What is your perspective of God today?

_____

_____

_____

"Write the Vision and Make It Plain"

Habakkuk 2:2

What is your vision for your life, and how will it help advance the kingdom of God?

_____

_____

_____

_____

_____

_____

_____

_____

_____

_____

_____

_____

_____

_____

_____

_____

_____

_____

My Faith, My Walk

What actions or steps are you taking to ensure your vision?

_____

_____

_____

_____

_____

_____

_____

_____

_____

_____

_____

_____

_____

_____

_____

_____

_____

_____

_____

_____

My Faith, My Walk

How will you measure your progress?

_____

_____

_____

_____

_____

_____

_____

_____

_____

_____

_____

_____

_____

_____

_____

_____

_____

_____

Scriptures: Matthew 6:33, Matthew 11:28–29, Philippians 4:13, Philippians 4:19